ALEX THE HIPPO

Written by Adam Ybarra

An Imprint of The Tenacious Group

Alex The Hippo is an imprint of The Tenacious Group.
Text copyright © 2020 by Adam Ybarra.
Illustrations copyright © 2020 The Tenacious Group.

Library of Congress Cataloging-in-Publication Data is available.
ISBN 978-1-7348755-4-6

Today... I will be the best version of me.

Today... I will take care of my teeth.

Today... I will get my nutrition.

Today... I will care for my dog.

Today... I will give love and appreciation.

Today... I will set my mind to do well in school.

Today... I will respect my desk.

Today... I will play and have fun.

Today... I will ask my teacher for help.

Today... I will drink water to stay hydrated.

Today... I will get a new book to read.

Today... I will clean my desk before I go home.

Today... I will offer my help.

Today... I will wave good-bye.

Today... I will put my backpack away.

Today... I will complete my homework.

Today... I will wash my hands before dinner.

Today... I will eat my greens for nutrition.

Today... I will get ready for school.

Today... I will wash-up before bedtime.

Today... was a great day to be me.

The End

Printed in the USA
CPSIA information can be obtained
at www.ICGtesting.com
JSHW040154020923
47311JS00008B/50